VOL. II
EXPLORATION

PERSONAL ILLUMINATIONS

MY TRAVEL JOURNAL

MY TRAVEL JOURNAL

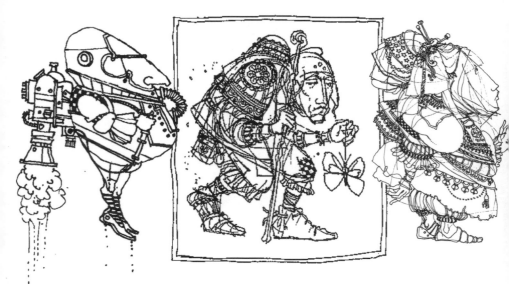

JAMES C. CHRISTENSEN

PERSONAL ILLUMINATIONS

VOL. II
EXPLORATION

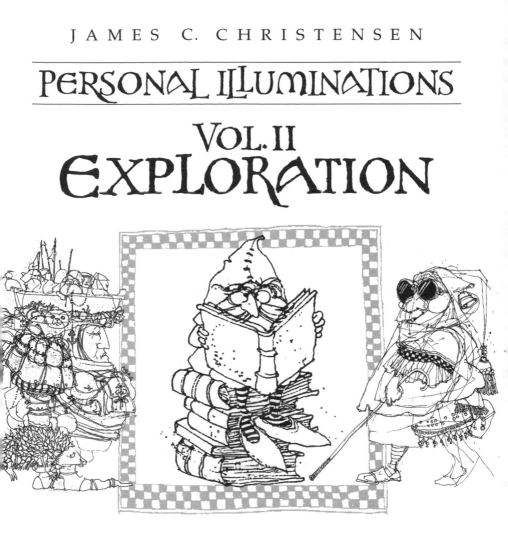

SHADOW
MOUNTAIN

Shadow Mountain is a registered trademark of Deseret Book Company.
Visit us at www.shadowmountain.com

ISBN 1-57345-856-2

OTHER BOOKS IN THE PERSONAL ILLUMINATIONS SERIES:
Imagination: My Creative Journal
Enumeration: My Book of Lists
Illumination: My Spiritual Journal
The Personal Illuminations Journal (hardcover)

Designed by Peter Landa and Milly Iacono
Printed in the United States of America

10   9   8   7   6   5   4   3   2   1

INTRODUCTION

J A M E S   C.   C H R I S T E N S E N

I carry a journal or sketchbook with me most of the time. Everything goes in there, from ticket stubs to ideas for new paintings, from memories to books I want to read and movies I want to see. When I travel to new places, my journal fills up with impressions, sketches, menus, memories, maps, and shopping lists. Because we have left our day-to-day lives temporarily behind, travel presents a unique opportunity for recording our experiences and reactions to new people and places.

So take this book with you and fill it up with your unique observations about your trip and about how what you observe might be changing you. You can paste in your train schedule, but remember to note in the margin how many women you counted wearing saris, or how many men played cards in each train car, or how many children stared at the color of *your* skin.

You don't have to leave the country to use this book, or even leave your state. All you need to do is start to notice how different people do the same things differently.

IT'S IMPORTANT TO GET OUT TO SEE NEW PLACES, EVEN IF YOUR HOME COULD BE MISTAKEN FOR A VACATION DESTINATION OR A FAIRY-TALE CASTLE.

TRAVEL LIGHT.
LEAVE THE EMOTIONAL BAGGAGE AT HOME.

THE FIRST RULE OF TRAVEL:  BE CURIOUS.

WHEN WE TRAVEL WE HAVE THE OPPOR-
TUNITY TO OBSERVE SOMETHING NEW
AT EVERY TURN. EVEN THE "GETTING THERE"
ON AIRPLANES, BUSES, SHIPS, AND TRAINS HOLDS
NEW EXPERIENCES IF YOU PAY ATTENTION.

WHAT HAPPENS ON THE WAY TO WHERE YOU'RE GOING?

TRAVEL THIRD-CLASS
TO EXPERIENCE A NEW CULTURE, STEP OUTSIDE THE HOTEL OR TOUR GROUP OR ORGANIZED PLAN FOR THE DAY.

TRAVEL IS LIKE THE THEATRE~YOU CAN GET A BOX SEAT AND HAVE A GREAT VIEW OF THE REHEARSED SHOW, BUT TO REALLY APPRECIATE THE LIFE OF THE THEATRE GO BACKSTAGE AND TALK TO THE ACTORS AND THE STAGECREW.

WHEN YOU TRAVEL DO THINGS
YOU MIGHT NOT DO AT HOME:
LOOK INSIDE OPEN WINDOWS

STARE (DISCREETLY)

PLAY STATUES

DON'T FEEL GUILTY ABOUT SITTING STILL IN
PUBLIC FOR LONG STRETCHES OF TIME. IT'S A
GREAT WAY TO REST YOUR FEET AND OPEN
YOUR EYES.

YOU HAVE TWO EARS
AND ONE MOUTH.
LISTEN MORE, TALK LESS.

COMMENTS OVERHEARD IN LINE TO SEE MICHELANGELO'S DAVID.

* HOW MANY of these DAVIDS DID MICHELANGELO CARVE?
* NO FLASH PLEASE
* IS THIS IT? IS THIS ALL THERE IS?
* HE'S NOT WEARING A FIGLEAF!!
* NO FLASH PHOTOS
* I FEEL LIKE THE TIN MAN – MY JOINTS NEED A LITTLE OIL
* I CRIED WHEN I SAW IT.
* NO FLASH
* WHY ARE YOU STOPPING AND READING EVERYTHING?

THE BEST THING ABOUT TRAVEL IS THAT IT CAN TURN ONE'S ASSUMPTIONS UPSIDE DOWN.

WHAT'S FOR BREAKFAST?
IN ISRAEL:
TURNIPS AND YOGURT
•
IN ENGLAND:
SMOKED KIPPERS
•
IN CHINA:
EEL PORRIDGE

As you start to notice new things, it's only natural to compare them to the way you live in your town, state, or country...
   "We never let the bulls loose in our town."

PLAZA DE TOROS
MADRID 20·MAY·80

Part of the fun of travel is noticing how different and varied people are.

WHAT IS NORMAL?
THEY THINK THEY ARE NORMAL AND YOU ARE STRANGE.

"COMMON SENSE IS A BUNDLE
OF PREJUDICES ACQUIRED BY THE AGE OF
EIGHTEEN."   ~ALBERT EINSTEIN

WHAT LOOKS STRANGE TO YOU
MAY BE PERFECTLY NORMAL IN
THE PLACE YOU ARE VISITING.

FIND OUT THE REASON WHY PEOPLE DO SOMETHING THAT SEEMS STRANGE TO YOU. SOMETIMES THERE IS NO PARTICULAR REASON, OR THE REASON IS SO OLD THAT MOST PEOPLE DON'T REMEMBER IT.

WHATEVER THE DIFFERENCES FROM YOUR OWN LIFE, YOU'LL PROBABLY FIND REMARKABLE UNIVERSALITY ABOUT IMPORTANT THINGS LIKE:

- KINDNESS - BABIES -
- ANCESTORS - SPIRITUAL AWE -

TRAVELING WITH CHILDREN

IS A BONUS. BABIES AND YOUNG CHILDREN ARE UNIVERSALLY ADORED AND HAVE A WAY OF BREAKING DOWN CULTURAL AND LANGUAGE BARRIERS.

BESIDES, FOR THEM EVERYDAY LIFE IS SO FRESH THAT NEW CULTURES AND CUSTOMS ARE JUST PART OF ANOTHER NEW DAY.

NO DAY IS WASTED IF YOU HAVE LAUGHED.

LEARN THE PACE OF LIFE AND THE PLACE OF CLOCKS IN THE CULTURE.

"MEET ME AT 4:00, SHARP."

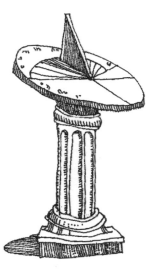

"I'LL BE BACK THIS AFTERNOON...
OR TOMORROW."

CUSTOMS CAN BE CONFUSING. LEFT HAND?
RIGHT HAND? BOW OR SHAKE?
STAND BACK AND WATCH HOW LOCALS DO IT.

CONSIDER HOW THE LOCALS SEE YOU.

Sunday 24 Aug 87 Went to Hyde Park Ward fr Church. Elder Tacke was witch and we got to hear him speak. Then we went to St Paul's while the was in the middle of a choral thing. We sat through it. The music was beautiful & the organ was un... Then I the alone was doing what I do on Saturday Mt. Then I & Susie & I walked about the town aplace up and back to Washington in St James Park.

A CORNER OF
ST. PAULS

SEE THEIR SACRED PLACES
THROUGH THEIR EYES.

WHAT'S ON THE MENU?
USUALLY WE LIKE TO KNOW WHAT'S ON THE MENU, BUT SOMETIMES WE CAN'T ASK, AND SOMETIMES WE DON'T WANT TO KNOW.

we spent the rainiest day of the trip at the National
Bird of Prey Center at Newent - as we drove there, the boys
were complaining about lunch, to pass the time, and Jon said
that we would eat at the cafe at the center - from there
the discussion turned to how many ways they
could serve owl!

A man at Newent about to
eat an owl sandwich

GRAND OPENING
THE TRELLIS RESTAURANT

OK, NOW I KNOW YOU WANTED LOBSTER FOR DINNER, BUT GUESS WHAT... WE GOT NO MORE LOBSTERS, ALL GONE, AAAND THE CHEF QUIT. AND I CAN'T FIND THE FORKS, BUT WE ACTUALLY REPLACED THE WHOLE KITCHEN LAST WEEK...

OOOH, MORE BAD NEWS, NO MORE CALAMARI. WHAT ELSE CAN I GET FOR YOU? IGNORE THE CRASHES FROM THE KITCHEN.

YOU KNOW WHAT, WE ARE OUT OF SCALLOPS NOW, HOW ABOUT A STEAK?

OK, WE GOT ONE STEAK LEFT, WHO GETS IT? YOU WANT CHICKEN? HERE ARE YOUR COKES, BUT THEY ARE FLAT. AND I FORGOT YOUR SHRIMP COCKTAIL, BUT THE SHRIMPS DON'T LOOK TOO GOOD ANYWAY. I WOULDN'T BLAME YOU IF YOU WENT SOMEWHERE ELSE FOR DINNER.... I'M GOING HOME NOW.

CHARMING GERMAN
FRAU WHO BREAKFASTED
WITH US AT HOTEL IN BRNO.

TAKE A BREAK IN THE BIG CITY

SIT IN THE MIDDLE OF THE TRAIN STATION OR AUTOMAT, BUS STOP, CASBAH OR BAZAAR. SKETCH OR WRITE A LITTLE ABOUT WHAT YOU SEE.

ALBARRACÍN

Even with rain, this has been a highlight of our trip! ALBARRACÍN is a beautiful village way off the beaten track out of TERUEL. Spain has made it a national treasure and UNICEO is looking at it as a world class location like CZESKY KRUMLOV. Narrow streets built on a narrow ridge of rock, it is very picturesque. We planned two days here, but the first it rained. Half the group returned to the hotel - 30 min walk from town. We painted all afternoon in our rooms. But the rain stopped in the afternoon and those that stayed did just fine. Next morning - sun! I took a lot of photos both days. In the afternoon we got on the bus and made the four hour trip to MADRID. Everyone is tired but doing well. I could come back to this place and spend a few quiet weeks being inspired.

LOCAL AUTHORITIES
KNOW WHAT THEY LOOK LIKE...
JUST IN CASE YOU NEED ONE.

A DAY AT THE BEACH CAN BE VERY DIFFERENT IN OTHER CULTURES. TO SUIT OR NOT TO SUIT...

CEREMONIES

WHAT'S DIFFERENT FROM YOUR CULTURE
AND WHAT'S THE SAME?

FOR THOSE CEREMONIES YOU CAN'T
FIGURE OUT, ASK SOMEONE.

CEREMONIES MIGHT BE BASED ON PARTS
OF THE CULTURE THAT AREN'T VISIBLE ANY-
MORE IN MODERN LIFE.

DEALING WITH DEATH

WHAT ARE THE CEREMONIES SURROUND-
ING DEATH? HOW DOES THE CULTURE
HONOR THEIR ANCESTORS, AND WHAT
DOES IT SAY ABOUT THEIR BELIEF IN LIFE
CYCLES AND ETERNITY?

Learn Local Legend

You can learn a lot about a culture from the stories that are passed down through generations.

Learn the geography, transfer of power among people and between peoples, who were "the enemy," and what was worth going to war over.

NOTICE THE RULES OF THE GAMES CHILD-
REN PLAY IN THE STREET OR IN THE FIELDS
OR IN THE PATCH OF DIRT THAT IS THE YARD.

FIND OUT WHOSE PICTURES ARE ON THE LOCAL CURRENCY.

WATCH LOCAL TELEVISION, EVEN IF YOU DON'T UNDERSTAND THE LANGUAGE. FIND OUT WHAT'S NEWS WHERE YOU ARE. AND WHAT DO THEY ADVERTISE?

WEATHER OR NOT...

WEATHER IS MORE THAN FINDING OUT IF YOU NEED TO CARRY A SWEATER OR UMBRELLA. NOTICE HOW THE AREA'S CLIMATE AFFECTS EVERYTHING:
- ARCHITECTURE • DIET • BUSINESS HOURS •
ORGANIZATION OF DAILY LIFE • EVEN ART

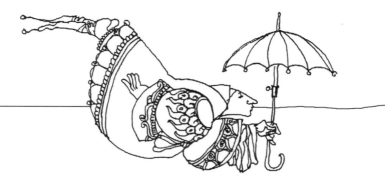

BUILDINGS AND GROUNDS

FOR ONE DAY, PAY PARTICULAR ATTENTION
TO DOORS (OR SPIRES OR GARGOYLES
OR BRIDGES).

WHAT DOES THE WAY THEY ARE BUILT
OR USED SAY ABOUT THE PLACE YOU
ARE VISITING?

GO TO THE PARK
HOW DO PEOPLE USE THEIR PUBLIC SPACES?

WATCH YOUR LANGUAGE
PLEASE • THANK YOU • POR FAVOR • DANKE •
MERCI • HSIEH, HSIEH • DOMO ARIGATO

EARLY MORNING BREAK

GO OUT AT DAWN TO SEE HOW DAILY LIFE
BEGINS IN YOUR NEW SURROUNDINGS.
VISIT THE FISH MARKET.

TALK WITH FARMERS OR STREET SWEEPERS.
GO TO A WATERING HOLE IN THE DESERT.
GO TO THE RIVER TO SEE WHO VISITS EARLY.

WHERE IN THE WORLD SHALL I GO NEXT?

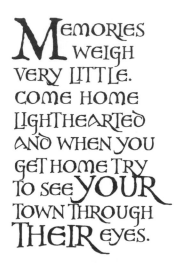

MEMORIES
WEIGH
VERY LITTLE.
COME HOME
LIGHTHEARTED
AND WHEN YOU
GET HOME TRY
TO SEE YOUR
TOWN THROUGH
THEIR EYES.